The Wise Mouse

written by Virginia Ironside

illustrated by Nick Sharratt

published by YoungMinds

YoungMinds Publications

Published by YoungMinds,
the children's mental health charity,
48-50 St John Street, London EC1M 4DG

www.youngminds.org.uk

First published 2003
3rd edition published 2007

Text copyright © Virginia Ironside, 2003
Illustrations copyright © Nick Sharratt, 2003

The moral right of the author has been asserted

Printed in England by AquatintBSC, London

British Library Cataloguing in Publication Data
A CIP catalogue record for this book is available from the British Library

ISBN 0-9545123-0-8

Maria didn't feel right.

Everyone else seemed to have happy families.

But she didn't.

And why? Well, her mum wasn't like other mums.
Oh, she looked like other mums, and sometimes
she was nice and kind. But there were times when
she seemed strange.

And that was what made Maria feel sad.

And angry.

And all muddled up.

One night, before she went to bed, she said to herself: "Oh, I wish my mum was like other mums!" And she cried herself to sleep.

But in the middle of the night she felt a little tap on her shoulder. She sat bolt upright. There, in the middle of her bed, was a friendly little mouse, sitting crossed-legged on her duvet.

"Good evening!" he said, holding out his tiny little paw. "I think you made a wish before you went to sleep, and I am here to help you. My name is Mouse."

Maria blinked. "Hello," she whispered. "I'm Maria."

"I'm very pleased to meet you," said Mouse. "How can I help?"

"Well," said Maria, "I just feel so miserable about my mum."

"I know all about mums," said Mouse. "I'm an expert. Good mums, bad mums, busy mums, lazy mums, mums with red hair and mums with curly hair. And did you know, no two mums are the same?

"Now tell me about your mum."

"Well, sometimes she behaves so oddly," said Maria.

"Sometimes she doesn't look after me properly...

"Sometimes she stays in bed nearly all day...

"Sometimes she thinks people are talking about her when they're not...

"Sometimes she hears things I can't hear...

"Sometimes she cries and cries...

"Sometimes she drinks too much...

"Sometimes she can't cook my dinner...

"Sometimes she says she loves me...

"Sometimes she says she hates me...

"Sometimes, well, some people say she's not right in her head - some laugh at her and say she's mental and mad because she does such strange things."

"I know what you mean," said Mouse, looking very wise. "You mean some people say she's got a mental illness?"

"Yes," said Maria. Then she worried when she thought about it being an illness. "Does it mean I can catch it?"

"Certainly not," said Mouse. "No one can catch a mental illness."

"But how can I make her better?" asked Maria. "I try so hard, I try to be good, I try to make things right for her. But nothing I do seems to make any difference - and that makes me very sad."

Mouse looked at Maria kindly. "I'm afraid the trouble is that nothing you do can make any difference, but there are adults who can help your mum. It's hard for her and hard for you when she is ill - but her illness is nothing to do with how you behave."

"But will she get better?" asked Maria.

"To be quite honest," said Mouse, "no-one quite knows. Some days she will feel better and some days she will still feel ill. Doctors and nurses look after ill people. They'll probably give your mum medicine to try to make her better and they'll talk to her about her illness. Talking is good don't you think?

"Sometimes the doctor might decide to take her into hospital for a little while but don't worry, she'll be home soon."

"What would happen to me if she went into hospital?" said Maria, worriedly. "I can't look after myself!"

"There'll always be someone to look after you," said Mouse. "There are kind families who look after children whose mums have gone into hospital; sometimes dads or an uncle or auntie or a friend's mum and dad look after children whose mums are in hospital.

"You wouldn't lose touch with your mum, anyway. She'll always be your mum, whatever happens."

"But I feel so muddled-up!" said Maria, starting to cry. "Sometimes I actually want her to go away forever! I did once stay with my auntie when mum was really ill and she cooked me my meals and got me to school on time, and I wanted to stay. I didn't seem to have so much to worry about then. But I'd be sad if I was away from mum all the time."

"Well, you know lots of us have two ideas in our head at the same time. You want her to go and you want her to stay. Sometimes you love her and sometimes you hate her. It's quite understandable," said Mouse.

"But why has this happened to ME!" shouted Maria, suddenly, feeling all panicky and angry, and jumping out of bed. "It's not fair!"

"It doesn't just happen to you, I'm afraid," said Mouse, sadly. "Lots of children have a mum or dad or brother or auntie or uncle or someone who has a mental illness.

"Thousands and thousands of them. You know, even mice can get mental illnesses!"

"But why do people get this horrible mental illness thing?" asked Maria. "Where does it come from?"

"It's hard to explain," said Mouse. "As you know, people's bodies can get ill but sometimes their minds can get ill, too. Sometimes medicine can help.

"Sometimes talking makes things better as well. But do remember there are special doctors who can help people with mental illness to get better.

"Sometimes people get better quite quickly. Sometimes it can take a long time."

"I feel so lonely," said Maria, sighing. "I can't have people round in case mum's being all funny and doing strange things, and I hate people talking about her. At school they sometimes tease me about her."

"It's because they don't understand," said Mouse. "People are often frightened of others who seem a bit different. I'm sure you know the feeling. Is there someone at school who you'd like to be your friend? Is there a teacher you can talk to?"

"I don't know that I want to find anyone," said Maria. "I don't like talking to other people about mum. I sometimes just sit on my own in the playground and feel sad. I often get angry and get into fights and sometimes I just cry."

"But isn't school nice now and then?" asked Mouse.

"Oh yes," said Maria. "I love swimming and P.E and school dinners. It's just that it seems as if everyone else at school has normal families."

"Oh ho ho! That's not true!" said Mouse, roaring with laughter. "I know at least ten people in your class who wish they had normal families:

"One's got a dad who drinks too much...

"Another's got a brother who takes drugs...

"Another's mum has a horrible temper...

"One's got a granny living with them who can't remember things...

"Everyone's got different problems. It's just that yours feel very big and frightening at the moment."

Maria got back into bed.

"Do you think I'm going to have a mental illness when I grow up?" she asked, suddenly alarmed.

"It's very, very unlikely," said Mouse. "You're you, and your mum's your mum."

Maria felt a bit better. But then she said: "I feel so frightened and sad sometimes. I wish I had someone ordinary to look after me."

"Your mum isn't always like this, remember," said Mouse. "She does have good times, too. And she always loves you, even if she can't show it when she's ill.

"And there are other people in your life who want to help you - your auntie or uncle or nan or grandpa. Or friends of the family. Or a nice teacher at school. Can you think of someone? Perhaps you could talk about your mum to them..."

Maria sighed. "I worry about mum so much."

"I do understand," said Mouse, "but really the best thing you can do is try to understand why your mum is ill and not to worry too much as there are lots of people to help you and your mum.

"Now, how do you feel?"

"Well," said Maria, wiping her eyes, "I think I do feel just a tiny bit better."

"Good," said Mouse. "And now it really is getting late so perhaps I better be off..."

"Oh, please don't go!" cried Maria. "I'll be all alone."

"Don't worry," said Mouse, patting her hand with his tiny paw. "As a special treat, I'll stay till you fall asleep. And remember there are people you can talk to when you feel sad or scared. Whenever you feel very worried or upset, put your hand in your pocket and imagine that I'm in there, doing my best to help."